OUR LORD'S LIFE

His Story in
Reverent Words and Original Paintings

OUR LORD'S LIFE

His Story in
Reverent Words and Original Paintings

by

AMELIA TONDINI MELGARI

Translated from the Italian by
Joy Mary Terruzzi

With Original Paintings by
Irina Kessler

HAWTHORN BOOKS INC
PUBLISHERS
New York

First American Edition 1960

CONTENTS

Saint Matthew	*page* I
Now Saint Luke tells us about his gospel	5
Saint John says to us:	7
Saint Mark says:	9
The Annunciation	I I
The visit to Saint Elizabeth	13
The bringing of the news to the shepherds	18
The presentation at the temple	22
Gold, frankincense, and myrrh	24
The massacre of the innocents	28
The flight into Egypt	31
The missing boy	33
Saint John the Baptist in the desert	39
The temptation of Jesus in the desert	42
In the temple of Nazareth	46
The miraculous draught of fish	48
The wedding at Cana	50
The pool of Bethsaida	52
Jesus and Nicodemus	55
The healing of the palsied man	57
The Sermon on the Mount	59
Other sermons of Jesus	62
The Roman centurion	65
The sower	66
Zacchæus	69
The widow of Naim	71
The calming of the tempest	73
The daughter of Jairus	74
The healing of the blind man	77

The miracle of the loaves   *page* 79
Saint Peter walks on the water   81
The Samaritan woman   82
The pearl   83
The lost sheep   84
The transfiguration   86
The healing of the lunatic boy   88
The healing of the deaf and dumb man   89
The good Samaritan   90
The prodigal son   93
Mary Magdalen   98
Martha and Mary   100
The widow's mite   103
The raising of Lazarus   104
Jesus drives the merchants out of the temple   106
The Pharisees against Jesus   108
The triumphal entry into Jerusalem   110
The Last Supper   112
Thursday evening   116
Jesus before the priests   125
Peter's denial   126
Jesus before Pilate and Herod   128
'Ecce homo'   132
Journey to the Cross   140
Christ is taken down from the Cross   148
The holy women before the sepulchre   151
Jesus appears to Mary Magdalen   153
A mysterious traveller   155
Jesus appears to the apostles   159
Thomas's lack of faith   162
Saint Peter   164
The Ascension   167

Matthew, Luke, John and Mark, sit on their golden thrones, in the Kingdom of Heaven, where they wait to tell us their wonderful story.

First, Matthew tells us about himself.

Saint Matthew

ONCE I was a tax-collector. I used to sit at my post by the lake at Capharnaum and see that the traders paid up their taxes. Those who did as I did were called publicans and were despised by the other Jews. One day I saw a very handsome man passing by. I asked those who were near me:

'Who is he?'

They answered:

'He is Jesus the Nazarene, a wonderful man: he heals the sick and he speaks words of great wisdom.'

That day when I first saw Jesus I did not think any more about the taxes. My thoughts kept returning to this man, to the light in his eyes and the tone of his voice. And I thought about him the next day and also during those which followed. I had only one wish: to see the man from Nazareth once again.

I saw him again. And he spoke to me, he said:

'Follow me.'

There was nothing in the world I wanted to do more. So I replied: 'Here I am.' And to celebrate this great event, I gave a farewell party that same evening at my home, and Jesus and his disciples came. Talking about this party afterwards, some of the Pharisees said to the disciples:

'Why does your master eat and drink with publicans like Matthew, and with sinners?'

Jesus overheard the remark and replied:

'Healthy people do not need a doctor, only those who are ill.'

Later on when I saw how he healed all those who suffered because their souls were starved of light I understood the truth of these holy words. I also wanted everyone but especially the Jews to know how good he was, so with God's help I wrote my Gospel. Because of this I am often portrayed with a pen in my hand, in front of an open book.

*Now Saint Luke tells
us about his gospel*

I WAS a Greek doctor. But as soon as I knew about Jesus, I realized how much better it is to cure the soul than the body. I was a disciple of Saint Paul, and I was also in prison with him in Rome. In my Gospel, I relate everything I managed to find out about Jesus from his friends. And who do you think must have recounted the story of his birth and babyhood? In my Gospel I make a special point of describing his kindness to women and to the poor. I have dedicated my book to all the converted, especially those who were pagans, in order to show that Jesus is merciful to all, whoever they be, and he always welcomes with joy those who turn to him. There is a calf beside me because in the beginning of my Gospel I tell of the priest Zachary performing his priestly duties before the Lord, and one of these duties was to offer a calf to the Lord.

5

Saint John says to us :

I AM John the Evangelist, brother of Saint James. My father was a fisherman. I greatly loved the company of John the Baptist, the son of Elizabeth. One day, while we were together, Jesus of Nazareth passed by us. At that moment my companion cried out:

'Behold the Lamb of God who takes away the sins of the world!'

I was surprised by these words and above all by the sight of Jesus. I followed him to his house and later on became his beloved disciple.

I lived to a great age and died at Ephesus, where I wrote my Gospel in Greek in order to explain the divinity of Jesus to the non-believers. My symbol is the eagle because my mind saw clearly and readily into the mysteries of the life of Jesus, seeing with the keen sharp vision of an eagle.

Saint Mark says:

I HAD the joy of knowing Jesus when I was still a boy. But I also knew the great sorrow of being present at his capture in the olive grove. I joined Paul, the apostle who preached the word of Christ everywhere. Then I was in Rome with Peter. One day the Christians said to me:

'Why do you not write down what Peter is always preaching in order to show that Jesus really is the Son of God?'

So I wrote the second Gospel. There is always a lion beside me because in my Gospel the lion is the symbol of the desert. My story begins in the desert with John the Baptist preparing the people for Jesus' coming much as, later in Rome, after our Lord's death, Peter preached about the coming of the Kingdom. And, I can assure you, it needed the courage of a lion to preach and teach in the Rome of the Emperor Nero.

The Annunciation

ONE day, at Nazareth, a humble maiden called Mary (which means 'Star of the Sea'), was praying in her little house on the sloping village street of Nazareth, when she heard a sound of wings. She raised her head and with great surprise saw a beautiful angel who said to her:

'Hail Mary, full of grace; the Lord is with thee; blessed art thou among women. . . .'

Mary did not understand these words, and she looked questioningly at the angel. Then the angel continued:

'Thou shalt bear a son and thou shalt call him Jesus.'

Mary, bewildered, then asked:

'But . . . whose son will he be?'

'He will be the Son of God: he will be the Saviour of the world.'

Mary, greatly moved, did not know what to say. When she was finally able to speak, she replied:

'I am the handmaid of the Lord. His will be done.'

Then the warm air of that soft morning must have been filled with a great sweetness, the olive trees, their silvered branches lightly stirring, seeming to say:

'Rejoice, poor suffering mankind. Your protector is coming. He will help the humble, the oppressed and the wretched and give them the peace that they so much desire.'

The swaying flowers of Nazareth, still damp with dew, the sparrows in their nests hidden among the palm trees, the swallows in the clear blue sky, the butterflies flying from flower to flower and the bees searching for nectar shared in the honour which God offered to this tiny planet. For God Himself was coming to live in it and bring back again the law of love.

Mary was still kneeling when the sun, high over the horizon, bathed her little house in a glory of light, which entered the open window, and rested on her head. Here was the perfect mother, humble and sinless, whom God had planned for Himself from all eternity.

The angel looked at her, wondering at the beauty and strength of her face. And he thought of the joy that she would feel when she clasped to her heart the baby who would be born to her.

Then the angel told her that one of her cousins, called Elizabeth, would also become a mother in a few months' time. And the angel disappeared.

The visit to Saint Elizabeth

MARY at once thought she should visit her cousin Elizabeth, to tell of her joyous news, to rejoice at hers and to give her all the help she needed. So one fine morning, as the sun rose above the horizon, Mary started off. Elizabeth lived in the hills, and the walk was long and weary; but Mary was so full of joy that she thought only of the angel's words.

'Mother of the Saviour of the world!' she said to herself. 'But what have I done to deserve so much grace?' And she already pictured herself with the divine Infant in her arms, gazing lovingly at the baby's sweet little face. 'And his Name shall be called "Jesus"' she repeated to herself, over and over, up hill and down dale.

Finally she reached her journey's end. Elizabeth saw her from a window of her house and ran to meet her with open arms, saying with great feeling:

'Blessed art thou among women, and blessed is the fruit of thy womb.'

Then she took Mary into her house and prepared a simple meal to refresh her; and all her actions displayed her devotion and admiration for the grace which the Lord had shown her cousin in choosing her to be the mother of the Saviour of the world.

Then Mary expressed her great joy in a very beautiful hymn which starts like this:

'My soul magnifies the Lord: my spirit has found joy in God, who is my Saviour . . .' and then she continued to praise God in these words: 'Praise be to the Lord who bestows on me, a humble creature, the grace of being the mother of the Almighty. From age to age I shall, therefore, be called blessed. By this gift to me, his humble handmaid, he wishes to show that he overlooks the powerful, and raises up instead the humble who believe in him. God has taken pity on the Jewish nation and is sending the Messiah whom he promised to our fathers centuries ago.'

Mary stayed a long time with Elizabeth and the two cousins spent many

happy days together talking of the babies which would be born to them. Then after about three months, Mary returned to her little house in the village street at Nazareth.

Saint Luke tells us in his Gospel: After some months, the Emperor Caesar Augustus ordered a census of his entire Empire. Because of this Joseph and Mary had to leave their home at Nazareth to go to Bethlehem and register their names.

Saint Matthew also speaks of this in his Gospel: You should know that Joseph was the husband of the Virgin Mary, but not the father of Jesus, who was the Son of God. Joseph knew this because an angel told him in a dream.

Saint Luke carries on with the story: The journey was long and tiring, especially for Mary who was about to become a mother; but they had to go. Finally one evening, after four long days of walking, they arrived at Bethlehem. Mary was exhausted. But how could they find a lodging if the city was full of strangers who had come for the census? Everywhere the innkeepers made the same disappointing reply: 'There is no room at the inn. It is no good asking. We are full up.'

Downcast, Joseph looked at Mary who could stand no longer.

He had to find shelter even if it was only in a cave. And so Joseph led Mary to a humble little stall where there were an ox and ass, and he gently made her comfortable on the straw.

16

Midnight came. There was the crying of a baby. And Mary was transfigured with joy for the divine child was born. The Saviour of the world, the King of kings, he who could have chosen a golden cradle and had at his disposal an army of servants, was warmed by an ox and an ass like the poorest of the poor.

The bringing of the news to the shepherds

IN the meantime some shepherds in the fields were watching their sheep who were sleeping peacefully.

'What a dreary life is ours!' exclaimed a shepherd. 'There is nothing but suffering and sadness in the world.'

'And will it always be so?' asked his neighbour.

'Oh, no. There will come . . .' but the sentence remained unfinished as the shepherds cried out in amazement. A vision of light came down from the sky.

It was an angel in a white robe, his wings outstretched and his arms

18

outspread. The shepherds knelt down on the earth and bowed their heads. Then the angel said: 'Do not be afraid: I bring you tidings of great joy. The Saviour of the world has been born today in David's city. And this is the sign: You will find a baby in swaddling-clothes, lying in a manger.'

Then, suddenly, a legion of the heavenly host appeared beside the angel singing: 'Glory to God in the highest and peace on earth to men of good will.'

The vision disappeared and the shepherds looked at each other amazed.

'Was it a dream?' they said.

'No, we have not dreamt,' replied the oldest. 'Did you not hear what the angel said about swaddling-clothes and a manger?'

They took some lambs as gifts and started off hurriedly to cover the two or three miles of their journey.

They were the first visitors to the Holy Child.

They found Jesus sleeping under the watchful gaze of his mother; with Joseph, protective and loving, beside them.

19

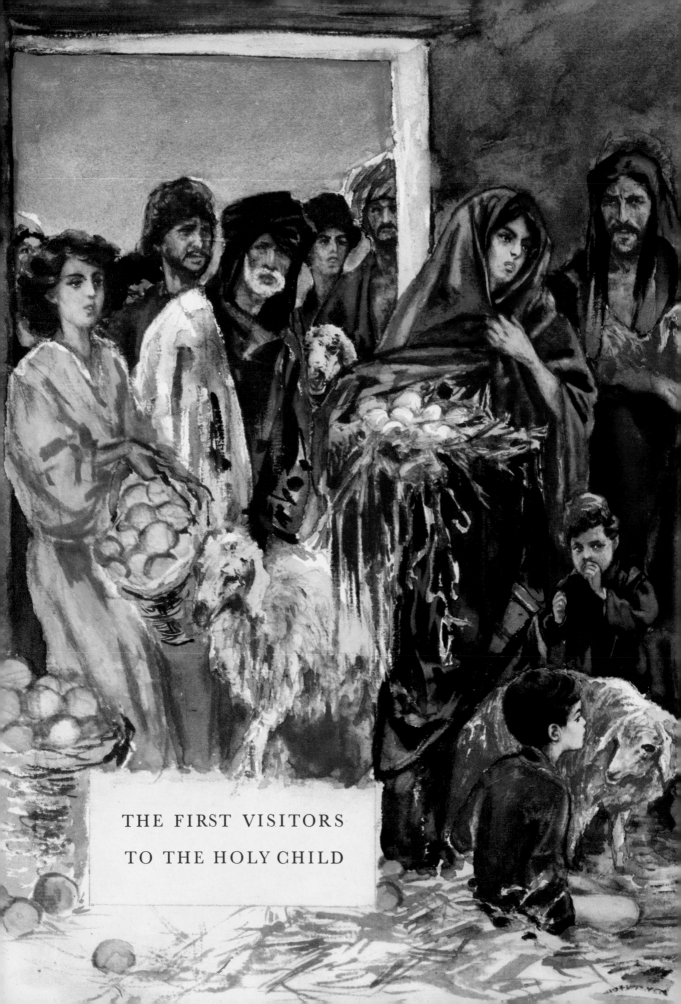

THE FIRST VISITORS
TO THE HOLY CHILD

The presentation at the temple

SAINT LUKE continues his story:

After forty days, according to the law of Moses, Mary, accompanied by Joseph, brought Jesus to the Temple at Jerusalem. She also brought two turtle-doves as an offering which was the custom for all the poorer people of those times. The rich offered a lamb. While preparations were being made for the ceremony, Simeon, an old man, well known for his wisdom, entered the Temple, approached Mary and looked at the baby whom she clasped to her heart. His face immediately lit up with joy. He took the tiny Jesus in his arms and said:

'Behold the Saviour of the world. Now that I have had the grace to see him I can die content.'

The old man had been guided to the Temple by the Holy Spirit who, some time before, had foretold to him that he would see the Messiah before he died.

Simeon then blessed Mary and Joseph and said that Jesus had a great destiny in store for him: he would condemn the non-believers, but would give life and resurrection to all the true followers of God. He would bring both grief and joy to the world. Then he turned sadly to Mary and added:

'Thou specially shalt suffer much. Thy heart will be pierced by a sword.'

Gold, frankincense and myrrh

NOW Saint Matthew speaks: I will tell of the visit of the Magi, wise men, keepers of ancient traditions, observers of the stars and men having much authority. They knew that the King of kings was destined to come on earth. Therefore on the night on which they saw a star brighter than all the others in the sky, they said:

'He is born. There is the sign.' They gathered together their servants, they saddled their dromedaries and camels, loaded them with rich gifts, and started off towards the point on the horizon where the star had appeared.

They crossed mountains and valleys, cities and villages, passing by poor houses, and rich palaces, and everybody gazed at them in amazement.

'Where is he that is born King of the Jews?' they asked everyone. They journeyed on faithfully, certain that they would have a sign on their arrival as they had been given a sign for their departure. News of their caravans entering Jerusalem reached King Herod, a wicked and cruel man who, fearing that the new king of whom so many spoke, would threaten his power, charged one of his ministers to call together all the learned men and doctors. He wanted to know the truth about these things. The minister carried out the command and so the king learnt that it really had been written in the book of a prophet: 'A leader who will govern the people of Israel will arise out of Bethlehem.'

Then Herod invited the Magi to his palace, and he questioned them closely about their journey, and afterwards said to them:

'On your return, come to me. Inform me of the road, so that I too may go and render homage to this new king.'

The Magi promised they would, and set off on their journey with only nine more miles to go. The very bright star reappeared and shone above

the hut where the divine child lay. The Magi looked at each other amazed.

'Can it be here?' they asked, perplexed.

They gazed in from the threshold and saw only a baby on his mother's knee. No gold, no silver, no precious cradle. But all the same they knew that they had come to the end of their search. Truth and beauty shone from the faces of this family and the welcome they gave had in it the goodness of God.

The three kings knelt down and offered their gifts: gold, frankincense, and myrrh. With these gifts they recognized Jesus as king, as God, and as man.

THE ADORATION

OF

THE MAGI

The massacre of the innocents

WHEN they returned the Magi did not go to Herod because an angel, in a dream, told them to change their route and not to let themselves be seen by the cruel king. But Herod was filled with jealousy because of the rumours concerning the greatness and power of the new king, and when he realized that the wise men would not return to bring him information, he ordered that all children born at that time in Bethlehem and the surrounding district should be killed.

28

Imagine the horror of those mothers when they saw their babies whom they loved so dearly torn from their arms and pierced by swords. Herod's soldiers carried out their orders ruthlessly. But Herod soon received his punishment because no one can escape God's wrath. He died a terrible death within a year after the massacre of those little children whose lives were given for the Holy Child.

29

The flight into Egypt

JESUS, however, escaped the massacre because an angel had appeared to Joseph in a dream and said to him:

'Rise up, take the child and his mother and bring them to Egypt and remain there until I tell thee, for Herod will seek the child to destroy him.'

So, once again in the depth of the night, by the light of the stars, Joseph saddled the ass, settled Mary in the saddle, placed the little Jesus in her

31

arms and, after saying good-bye to the hut which had given them hospitality the Holy Family took the road to Egypt.

We know nothing of the journey, neither the route they took nor how soon they felt safe from the possibility of being overtaken on the road by Herod's soldiers riding their swift Arab horses.

But we know they arrived happily in Egypt where they remained until an angel appeared once more to Joseph in a dream and told him that he could return because Herod was dead. But as Herod had been succeeded by his son, well known for his cruelty, Joseph brought them north to Nazareth where Jesus, the Nazarene, passed the rest of his childhood.

The missing boy

SAINT LUKE now tells us about Jesus as a boy: Every year on the occasion of the Feast of the Passover, Joseph and Mary went to Jerusalem where great festivities were held in the Temple. And when Jesus was twelve years old they took him also. On the return journey from Jerusalem, Joseph and Mary discovered that he was no longer with them. Alarmed, they looked for him everywhere, along the highway, in the caravans, outside the walls and in the city. At the end of three days they began to search the courts of the Temple.

There was Jesus, seated in the midst of the doctors, who were the official teachers of catechism, and he was asking them such profound questions that all who heard him were amazed.

Mary said sadly to him:

'My son, why hast thou done this? For three days we have been anxiously seeking thee.'

And Jesus answered:

'When you missed me you should have guessed I would be in the Temple, which is my Father's house, and so you would not have felt anxious.'

Then, as an obedient son, he returned to Nazareth with Joseph and Mary.

At Nazareth, Jesus grew up: handsome, strong and healthy. He helped Mary in the little household tasks, and he helped Joseph in the carpenter's shop: planing, gathering the wood shavings, and polishing, just as any other boy would have done. In his free time he played with his companions: and with them he was always full of life, generous, and kind.

35

As the Son of Mary, he grew like all the other boys, but Mary knew that he was also the Son of God and watched over him continuously with love and apprehension. She thought of Simeon's prophecy and she felt worried: not for herself, but for that which was in store for her son.

Jesus stayed with his mother until he was about thirty years old, then he left her in order to start his mission.

Saint John the Baptist in the desert

SAINT LUKE reminds us of Mary's cousin, Elizabeth. As you remember, the house of Elizabeth was also to be gladdened by the birth of a baby. That baby, when he was born, was called John, and when he grew to manhood he left his home and went about preaching in a loud voice that the time for repentance had come, and telling people to prepare the way of the Lord because the Kingdom of Heaven was at hand. John wore a camel skin fastened round his loins by a girdle, and he ate locusts and wild honey.

The people of Jerusalem and of all Judea hurried in great numbers to listen to him, confessing their sins, and begging John to baptize them: this he did, as they stood in the river Jordan. But he said:

'After me will come one who is mightier than I. One whose shoes I, though prostrated on the ground, am not worthy to untie. I baptize you with water, but he will baptize you with the Holy Ghost.' He was right. John was the forerunner of Jesus.

But one day a strange thing happened, which filled John and all those present with amazement and awe. Jesus himself went to the bank of the Jordan and asked to be baptized.

'But how can I baptize thee?' said John humbly. 'Thou art perfection and hast no need to be purified. I only prepare the way of the Lord, and thou art the Lord himself.'

But Jesus, with his compelling and yet gentle voice, replied:

'Do not question me, John. It is better that thou dost what I tell thee.' Then he went down into the water of the Jordan; and John obediently baptized him.

But this amazing event was not yet concluded. Suddenly the clear blue heavens opened, and high up in the sky there appeared a dove with pure white wings. It hung motionless a moment, and then descended slowly, resting over Jesus, while at the same time these words were distinctly heard from the heavens:

'This is my beloved Son in whom I am well pleased.'

That dove was no other than the Holy Spirit who had taken the form of the beautiful winged creature in order to come down upon the beloved son of the Eternal Father. So the Holy Trinity was shown in three perfect signs to men: the Father's voice, His Son become man, and the Holy Spirit in the form of a dove.

The temptation of Jesus in the desert

THE same Holy Spirit brought Jesus into the desert where, tempted by the devil, he showed men how to overcome temptation. When the devil first appeared to Jesus, who had fasted for forty days, he said to him:

'If thou be the Son of God, command that these stones be made bread.'

But Jesus replied:

'Man shall not live by bread alone; but by every word that proceedeth out of the mouth of God.'

42

Then the devil brought him to the highest pinnacle of the Temple and said to him:

'If thou be the Son of God, then cast thyself down. The angels will hold thee up.'

But he replied:

'It is written again, Thou shalt not tempt the Lord thy God.'

Then the devil took him up to a very high mountain, showing him the magnificence of the kingdoms of the world, and saying to him:

'All these things I will give thee if thou wilt fall down and worship me.'

And Jesus replied:

'Get thee hence, Satan. Thou shalt worship the Lord thy God and him only shalt thou serve.'

The devil fled and the angels brought comfort to Jesus.

45

In the temple of Nazareth

JESUS, who had already been preaching for some time and had also started to work miracles, wished to bring his word also to Nazareth, to the land where he had spent his childhood. And he went there with great eagerness. He saw once again the house where he had spent many quiet years, and met the companions of his carefree childhood. Arriving at Nazareth he waited for the Sabbath, then went to the synagogue to preach. They brought him the book of the Prophet Isaias. He opened it, and then began to explain it: and he explained it so well that all marvelled at what they heard.

They had not expected so much wisdom from him. They said:

'But is not this the son of Joseph the carpenter?'

'It is he all right. And his relations are here also.'

Among other things Jesus said:

'The Spirit of the Lord is upon me. He has sent me to bring liberty to the prisoners, to give sight to the blind, to give peace to the oppressed. . . .'

Then he added: 'You will certainly ask: "And why dost thou not do these marvellous things here in thy native city?" It is because of your want of faith in me.'

At these words the other Nazarenes who were in the synagogue took offence and were angry: they railed against Jesus, forcing him to leave the synagogue, and hunting him out of the city, and they took him up the street to the top of the hill in order to cast him down.

But Jesus did not fear their wrath. He looked at them quietly, and then, just when they were about to push him into the void, he passed through the midst of them, with the greatest calm, and went on his way.

The miraculous draught of fish

AND now—says Saint Luke—I will speak to you of the miraculous draught of fish, one of the most beautiful episodes in the life of Jesus. This is how it was:

The divine Master was followed by a daily increasing crowd of the poor, who found comfort in his words for all their ills, and would not leave him. One day, followed by this multitude, he happened to come to the shore of the Lake of Genesareth, and saw two boats with some fishermen who were drawing in their nets. But these men were disappointed with their catch which had been very poor.

So Jesus said to the owner of one of the boats, a certain Simon:

'Take me out in the boat and anchor a little way from the shore so that I may speak to the crowd.'

48

Simon obeyed and Jesus, not far from the water's edge, began to address the multitude.

When he had finished speaking, he said to Simon:

'And now go into deep water and cast the nets.'

Simon, shaking his head, replied:

'Oh, Lord, it is useless; we have fished all night and caught nothing. There is no catch in the lake today.'

But it was impossible to disobey Jesus. So Simon went into deep water and threw the nets. Then the miracle occurred. When the nets were drawn in again they were so full that they could hardly be pulled into the boat. Simon was speechless with astonishment. Then he joyfully invited the other fishermen left on the shore to join him. Thus the second boat also was filled with fish. Simon understood then that this was indeed a miracle; and knowing himself to be unworthy of so great a kindness threw himself at Jesus's feet, exclaiming:

'Lord, keep away from me for I am a sinner.' But Jesus lifted him up gently and said to him:

'Do not be afraid. Henceforth thou shalt be a fisher of men.'

Simon it was who later confessed Jesus to be 'the Christ, the Son of the Living God'. Our Lord renamed him Cephas or Peter, which means 'Rock' because he was to be the firm foundation on which Christ would build his Church.

The wedding at Cana

NOW Saint John tells us about the first miracle of Jesus. Three days later, Jesus, his mother and the disciples were invited to a wedding feast at Cana in Galilee. The bridal couple had prepared a great banquet, and there were many guests. The feast took place as arranged, with much rejoicing.

All at once Mary realized that the wine was running short. It was very embarrassing for the hosts; they certainly could not serve water at such a grand feast. The servants looked at each other, not knowing what to do.

50

Then Mary, always willing to give her help, turned to Jesus and said to him:

'There is no more wine.'

The words were common enough, but they hid a great prayer: Thou who canst do all, remove this embarrassment from these worried people. From the reply he gave, it seemed that Jesus did not want to perform a miracle at that time.

Yet Mary looked into her son's eyes with all her love and immense faith, and said to the servants:

'Do whatever Jesus tells you.'

Then Jesus called the servants and pointed out six big jars which had been prepared for the ceremonial washing before the feast, and he ordered that they be filled with pure water. The servants obeyed at once.

'And now give it to the guests to drink,' said Jesus.

The servants, to their great surprise, discovered that instead of water they were pouring out wine. And it must have been very good wine since all the guests paid the highest compliments to the hosts. Then the master of the feast went up to the bridegroom and said to him:

'Thou hast not done as others do who serve the good wine at the beginning of the meal when everybody has a clear head and can judge it; but thou hast kept the best for the end.'

At first the bridegroom did not know what to say. But then he realized, as did all the others also, that it was a miracle.

Thus Jesus, at Cana in Galilee, began the miracles which were to amaze all the world.

The pool of Bethsaida

SAINT JOHN tells us more about the miracles.

One day Jesus went up to Jerusalem where the Jews were celebrating a feast. On that occasion many sick people had been carried to the pool of Bethsaida which was just beside the city, to be cured.

At a certain moment an angel of the Lord would come down and stir up the water.

The first sick person to enter the water which had been stirred up would regain his health.

There was, among others, a man who had been ill for thirty-eight years, lying on his bed, despairingly awaiting his turn. The others always reached the pool ahead of him.

Then Jesus said to him:

'Dost thou wish to become well again?'

The sick man answered:

'Oh Lord, if it be thy wish. . . . But I cannot. I am helpless on this bed, and no one bothers to let me down into the pool during the stirring of the water. All go in and I can only look on.'

Gently Jesus said to him:

'Rise up and walk.'

The sick man felt himself healed at that very moment.

He joyfully arose and, after having thanked Jesus warmly, went on his way.

Jesus and Nicodemus

AMONG the Pharisees there was a Jew called Nicodemus who often thought of the miracles that Jesus performed but was unable to understand them because he did not yet believe that Jesus was the Son of God.

Many times as he walked along the paths of his garden thinking of the strange powers of Jesus, he must have said to himself:

'But how can he change water into wine, restore sight to the blind, hearing to the deaf and the use of their limbs to the paralysed? How can he do these things by his own power?'

One day he saw Jesus passing by, surrounded by a crowd. The divine Master was walking slowly, the sun shining on his head. The eager crowds were around him, all talking at once and trying to touch his robe.

Nicodemus could not drag himself away from the window, while amazement, doubt, admiration, and disbelief all battled in his soul as clouds alternate with a clear sky on a spring day.

Suddenly he decided to go to Jesus and hear his words.

But he did not yet have enough courage to follow him with the crowd. He wanted to speak to him privately, and in a quiet place to open his soul to him in confidence.

He waited for nightfall. Then he wrapped himself in a dark cloak and went to Jesus.

Jesus received him gladly and listened to him with great kindness.

Thus Nicodemus also came to understand the generosity of God who so loved us that he sent his only Son on earth to save us and give us eternal life.

In the quiet of that night Jesus explained to him how this new life would be given to us by baptism. By the pouring of water in his name, his followers would become the adopted Sons of God. The learned Nicodemus found this a big mystery, but from what happened after Jesus was crucified we know that he learnt to believe.

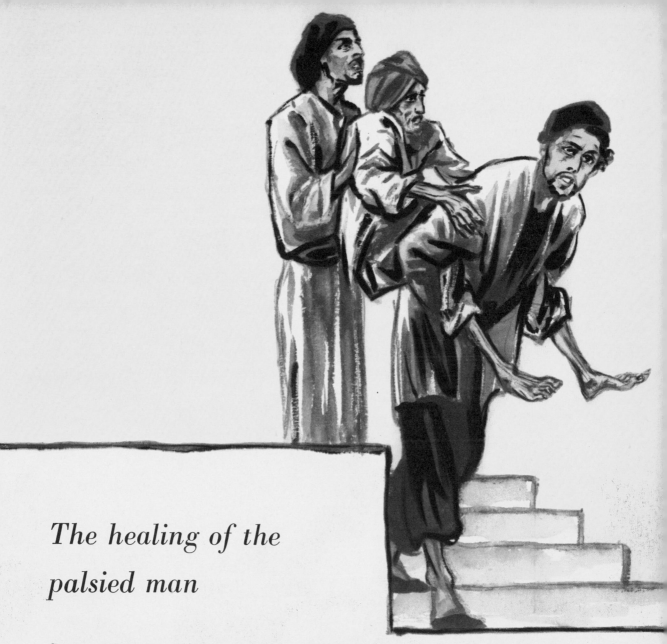

The healing of the
palsied man

SAINT MATTHEW, Saint Mark, and Saint Luke all tell us in their gospels of the miracle of the healing of the palsied man.

One day Jesus was praying in a house. A vast multitude had come to listen to him. Four men also came carrying a palsied man on a bed and, as they were prevented from entering by the great throng, they went up on to the flat roof, made a hole in it and lowered the palsied man down into the room where Jesus was. The sick man who had thus proved his faith, looked imploringly at the divine Master, afraid to speak. Jesus, seeing their faith, said to the sick man:

'Son, thy sins are forgiven thee.' Then some of the Scribes thought to themselves: 'He is blaspheming, who can forgive sins but God only.' Jesus read their thoughts and asked them: 'Which is easier, to say "thy sins are forgiven" or "arise and walk"? But it will show you that the Son of Man has power in earth to forgive sins.' Then he turned to the paralytic and said: 'Arise, take up thy pallet and go home.' So he got up immediately, took his own pallet and went home, glorifying God.

The Sermon on the Mount

NOW Saint Matthew and Saint Luke both tell us about the sermon on the mount.

Jesus, to avoid meeting the Pharisees who were always hostile to him, withdrew to the south of Capharnaum, and his disciples followed him. One evening, however, he wished to remain alone, and he retired to a nearby mountain side where he spent the whole night in prayer.

Then, in the morning, he was joined by his disciples and from among them he chose the twelve nearest to his heart, calling them Apostles, which means 'Messengers of the Lord'. He then began to teach them his doctrine.

He said:

'BLESSED ARE THE POOR IN SPIRIT FOR THEIRS IS THE KINGDOM OF HEAVEN.

'BLESSED ARE THE MEEK FOR THEY SHALL POSSESS THE LAND.

'BLESSED ARE THEY THAT MOURN FOR THEY SHALL BE COMFORTED.

'BLESSED ARE THEY WHO HUNGER AND THIRST AFTER JUSTICE FOR THEY SHALL HAVE THEIR FILL.

'BLESSED ARE THE MERCIFUL FOR THEY SHALL OBTAIN MERCY.

'BLESSED ARE THE CLEAN OF HEART FOR THEY SHALL SEE GOD.

'BLESSED ARE THE PEACE-MAKERS FOR THEY SHALL BE CALLED THE CHILDREN OF GOD.

'BLESSED ARE THEY THAT SUFFER PERSECUTION FOR JUSTICE' SAKE FOR THEIRS IS THE KINGDOM OF HEAVEN.'

How blessed is that mountain from which the divine words of Jesus were carried over the seas, the mountains, and the plains; these divine words which even today still help and always will help us to bear life's troubles; words which give a comfort in sorrow, and assure us of divine mercy. For only by the following of Jesus here on earth can we come to merit eternal happiness in the Kingdom of Heaven.

There are many wise men in this world who, when others treat them unjustly, would like to rebel; but they do not do so, quietly accepting the injustice, because they know that Jesus, in the sublime words pronounced on the Mount, assures them of the rewards they will receive from God himself. We know, of course, that to learn to bear suffering, we must pray much, and with humility, and the greatest proof God gave of this was in choosing Mary, the gentle maid of Nazareth, from among all women, as the virgin mother of his divine Son.

Humility is the subject of one of the most beautiful parables of Jesus.

Once, two men went to the Temple to pray. The first, a Pharisee, proudly prayed aloud with his head held high:

'I thank thee, Lord, that thou hast made me wise and honest and not like this publican; I never do wrong; I do my duty towards other men.'

But the other, a publican, stood with bowed head, beat his breast as a sign of humility and said:

'Lord, have pity on me, a sinner.'

The prayer of the Pharisee had no value in God's eyes and displeased him, while he loved the humble publican for his humility and heard him with joy because whoever raises himself up will be humbled, and he who humbles himself will be raised up.

One must pray not only with humility, but also with perseverance and great faith. One must never forget that God is our Father and, as a merciful Father, is always ready to satisfy the wishes of his children when they are just and not contrary to the salvation of their souls. He does what any loving father would do. If a small boy asked his father: 'Can I have that eel?' his father would certainly refuse if it was not really an eel at all, but a snake.

Later on a day will come, perhaps after many years, when the child will understand why God our Father rightly refused the request made so long ago, and then he will say joyfully:

'I am also grateful, Lord, for what you denied me. You were right. You alone are always right.'

Prayer is a gold thread which unites suffering humanity with him who alone can give peace, and the true joy which lasts for ever.

OTHER SERMONS OF JESUS

Other sermons of Jesus

THEN Jesus continued preaching his doctrine to the disciples and to the
humble people who had come from the mountains, the plains, and the
shores of the sea to be revived by his words as one is revived in the spring
by the rays of the sun.

He said: 'I am the Light of the world. I am the Way, the Truth and the
Life. Whoever believes in me shall have eternal life. Because eternal life
is just this: that man should know the Father and that they should know
that I am sent by the Father.'

He exhorted them to have great faith in Divine Providence. God
knows the needs of all his creatures and takes care of everything. By
creatures he means not only human beings, but also flowers, plants, birds,
and insects. He said: 'Look at the birds of the air, they do not sow, or
reap or gather grain into barns. And yet your heavenly Father sees that
they are fed. Look at the lilies of the field; they do not spin or weave; but
even Solomon in all his glory was not arrayed like one of these.'

He exhorted men to keep close to him because he alone can give the
spiritual guidance and support necessary for living in God's grace.

He explained his meaning in these simple words: 'I am the vine and you are the branches. If a branch is not united to the vine, it cannot bear fruit.'

He also said: 'Whoever wishes to be my disciple, must deny himself, take up his cross and follow me.' With Jesus as our captain we will have courage to say 'No' to what is wrong, and will freely accept any sacrifice so as to follow him on the road which leads to glory. He exhorted us to pray with faith: 'Have faith in God. . . . In truth I say to you: if you have faith and do not hesitate . . . even if you should say to this mountain— Remove thyself from here and be cast into the sea, it will be done.' We can obtain that which seems impossible by a prayer that is truly meant. He exhorted us to help the poor, to visit the sick, to treat all suffering people gently and he said: 'Even a cup of cold water given in my name shall have its reward.'

In fact no one is more generous than Jesus and he amply rewards those who succour the poor, who are so especially dear to his heart.

He exhorted men to be content if they had enough for their daily needs and not to pile up riches on earth. The riches which they should try to accumulate are spiritual ones, which would prepare them a place in the heavenly Kingdom. Here are his words: 'Do not try to accumulate treasure on earth, where rust and moths will consume it and where thieves may steal it. Give alms, and so accumulate instead a great treasure for yourself in heaven, where thieves cannot take it and moths cannot reach it. Because where your treasure is, there will your heart be also.'

He promised comfort to the men who followed his law. He said: 'Come to me, all you who labour and are burdened and I will refresh you. Take my yoke upon you and learn from me who am meek and humble of heart, and you will find peace in your soul; because my yoke is sweet and my burden light.'

Jesus loved children very much.

One day the disciples asked him: 'Who is the greatest in the Kingdom of Heaven?'

And Jesus calling a little child, placed him in the midst of them, and said: 'Believe me: if you do not become like little children, you will not enter the Kingdom of Heaven. Those who humble themselves as little children will be the greatest in the Kingdom of Heaven. And he who welcomes such a little child in my name, welcomes me.'

He preached goodness and purity of heart. He said: 'It is not what enters the mouth that makes a man impure, but what comes out of it.' His meaning was: The food which men swallow can sometimes harm the body, but this is nothing in comparison to the harm which can be done by words which come out of the mouth. Because what comes out of the mouth comes from the heart; and if a man's heart is not pure he will lose God's grace and live sinfully.

He said that we are all brothers and must love one another and bear with one another and he who is angered with his brother commits a sin.

He said: 'One must not judge anyone hardly for as we judge others, so will we be judged by God. We should be severe with ourselves, but indulgent towards others.' He preached love even towards enemies.

'It is easy to love those who love us and do us good; but we must also love those who do us harm.'

And again:

'If someone needs your help, give it with pleasure, without expecting any reward. And be careful not to do good works just in order to be praised. Do good silently without letting others know about it. You will have your reward from the heavenly Father.

'If you do that which I teach you, you will be as that wise man who built his house on rocks. Floods came, winds blew, storms raged, but the house remained intact because it was built on a solid and secure foundation.

If instead you do not do that which I tell you, it will happen to you as it did to the fool who built a house on sand. At the first gust of wind the house collapsed and the fool was left homeless.

64

The Roman centurion

ONE day a Roman centurion came to Jesus and asked him to cure his sick servant of whom he was very fond. Jesus replied to him: 'I will come to thy house.' But the centurion said humbly:

'Lord, I am not worthy that thou shouldst enter into my house; only say but one word and my servant will be healed.'

Jesus was gladdened by so much faith and said to the centurion: 'Go. Thy faith has already saved thy servant.' And the centurion went home and found his servant healed.

65

The sower

JESUS often spoke in parables, simple stories which, with a few words of explanation, could be understood by all. This tale is told us by three of the evangelists: Saint Matthew, Saint Mark, and Saint Luke.

One day Jesus was on the sea shore, surrounded by an immense crowd of people who were waiting to hear his words of faith and love. So he went aboard a small boat and spoke the following parable:

'One day a sower went out to sow. As he scattered the grain it was blown about by the wind. Some of the seed fell between stones where the earth was dry and poor; the shoots sprang up, but they soon died for lack of nourishment; some fell among thorns and were smothered; some fell on good soil, and at harvest time yielded a quantity of fine ears of wheat.'

At first those present were unable to understand the meaning of the parable and so Jesus explained: 'The seed is the word of the Lord. If those who listen are distracted and do not pay attention to it, the word is lost,

66

like the seed eaten up by the birds, and the earth remains dry and poor. Then there are those who listen but the devil comes and takes the word away from their hearts, and they are like the seed that fell by the roadside for no one can be saved unless he believes.

The seed that fell among the stones is the word of God in the soul of those who only listen, without trying to put the precious teachings into practice. At the first difficulty they are lost because the word has not taken firm root. The seed that fell among the thorns is the word of God which is choked by the love of worldly goods. These keep it from the light of truth.

But the seed that fell on good earth is the word of God in the souls of those who know how to receive and cultivate it. It yields unhoped for fruits of grace, so that these people gradually become more and more like Christ in their characters. Some are good Christians, some are better and some are best.

Zacchæus

IT is only Saint Luke who tells us about the following:

The rich man, Zacchæus, was one of the leading publicans of Jericho.

As Jesus came down the road into that steaming, low-lying city, Zacchæus forgot the heat, forgot his dignity, and ran on ahead to climb into a sycamore tree. For, otherwise, how could a squat little man like himself hope to see over the tall headdresses of his fellow citizens.

He had a good view. Jesus passed right beneath the branches and suddenly looked up. 'Zacchæus,' he said, showing that he knew his name, 'make haste and come down for I want to stay in thy house.' So Zacchæus clambered down quickly and gave Jesus a great welcome to his home.

The crowd murmured, as usual, about Jesus being the guest of a sinner. But the sinner himself felt compelled by our Lord's very presence to mend his crooked ways. He came and stood before Jesus and said:

'Half my property is going straight to the poor. Out of the rest of it I will pay four times the amount to anyone whom I have cheated.'

That is why Jesus rejoiced saying: 'Saving grace has come to this house today.'

69

The widow of Naim

SAINT LUKE tells us about the miracle.

One day Jesus, followed by a great multitude, was going towards a city eight miles south-east of Nazareth. But just as he was about to enter the town he and his followers had to stop to allow a sad procession to pass on its way.

It was the funeral of the only son of a widow.

The poor mother was grieving as she followed her son's bier.

The coffin-bearers stopped as soon as they saw Jesus followed by the huge crowd.

He looked at the unhappy mother with great compassion, and going up to her, said:

'Do not weep any more.'

Then he touched the bier with these words:

'I say to thee, rise up.'

The boy who had been lying there rigid with no sign of life, immediately obeyed. He got up, gazing lovingly at Jesus, and saw in amazement the coffin-bearers, his mother in tears, and all the people who accompanied the funeral procession. He smiled, and started to speak.

Then Jesus restored him to his mother, who was overcome with joy and amazement, and did not know how to thank Jesus for what he had done.

But a sudden shout rose from the disciples, from the crowd gathered round the boy, and from all who had been present at the miracle:

'A great prophet has risen up amongst us' and 'God has visited his people.'

For some time afterwards, everyone talked of this miracle, and the news spread like lightning all over Judea and beyond.

The calming of the tempest

AFTER spending a long day teaching parables to a huge crowd, Jesus was crossing the lake of Genesareth with his apostles. Suddenly a furious storm arose and the waters became very rough. Jesus was fast asleep in the stern of the boat with his head on a cushion. The apostles did their best to bring the boat to the shore, but it was beyond them for great waves surged on every side. Then, terrified, they turned to Jesus and awoke him, crying out:

'Master, save us for we are lost!'

He opened his eyes, looking calmly at his apostles and saying:

'Why are you so frightened?'

Then he ordered the wind and the waters to be still, and immediately there was absolute calm on the lake. The apostles looked at each other in astonishment and said:

'Who is this whom even the wind and the water obey?'

73

The daughter of Jairus

SAINT LUKE now tells us the story of Jairus's daughter.

Jesus had just returned from one of his many journeys during which he performed numerous miracles, and he was on the shore surrounded by a great multitude. Suddenly he saw the ruler of the synagogue, a certain Jairus, anxiously hurrying towards him. On reaching Jesus,

74

Jairus threw himself at his feet, imploring him to heal his twelve-year-old daughter who was dying.

Jesus arose and went with Jairus towards the house where the sick girl lay. The crowd followed him so closely as almost to impede his walking.

Among the multitude was a woman who had been sick for a long time and whom no doctor had been able to cure. This woman, guided by her great faith, touched the hem of Jesus's garment and she was immediately healed.

Jesus asked, 'Who touched me?'

Then the apostles said to him:

'Master, dost thou ask who touched thee when the crowd is pressing on all sides?'

But Jesus replied:

'No. Someone touched me seeking to receive a favour.'

Then the healed woman threw herself at Jesus's feet, begging his forgiveness and telling him of the grace she had been granted.

In the meantime there arrived a man, breathless with running, who went up to Jairus and said:

'It is useless to trouble the Master further, for thy daughter is dead.'

But Jesus looked at the despairing father, and said:

'Do not be afraid. Have faith.'

When they arrived at Jairus's house, the Master entered, followed only by the head of the house and Peter, James, and John.

The mother was weeping beside the girl's bed.

Jesus went up to her, saying gently:

'Do not cry. She is not dead, but only sleeping.'

Everyone looked at him in doubt, but he took the girl by the hand and said: 'Sit up, my child.' And she obeyed him.

'And now,' said Jesus to the astonished parents, 'give her something to eat.'

The healing of the blind man

HERE is the story of a miracle told by Saint Mark.

At Jericho there was a blind man, Bartimeus, who used to sit at a street corner begging for alms. And he used to think: Oh, if only I could see like other men. If Jesus of Nazareth should pass by I would ask him for this grace.

One day he felt a great crowd around him and asked:

'What is happening?'

They answered him:

'Jesus of Nazareth is among us.'

Then the blind man started shouting:

'Jesus, Son of David have pity on me! Jesus, have pity on me!'

The people near him told him to be quiet, but Jesus turned towards the beggar and asked him:

'What dost thou desire?'

'Lord,' replied the blind man, 'make me see.'

And Jesus said to him:

'Go thy way, thy faith hath saved thee.'

And at once he completely regained his sight.

He followed Jesus along the road glorifying God; and the people, seeing that he was cured, praised God too.

The miracle of the loaves

THIS miracle is told by all the evangelists in their books. Saint Matthew tells us:

Jesus had retired to a place in the desert, but a great crowd followed as usual. For three days these people remained near Jesus, and the apostles said to him: 'We must send the multitude away so that they can obtain some food.'

Jesus replied: 'It is not necessary.'

A boy had five barley loaves and two small pickled fish. (It is John the fisherman who tells us the Greek name for them.) So Jesus asked for them, and blessing them, he broke them and ordered his disciples to divide them out among the multitude. There were more than five thousand people there and all ate their fill and the pieces of bread left over filled twelve baskets.

79

Saint Peter walks on the water

THE evening of the same day, Jesus told the disciples to go on ahead while he sent away the crowd, and then withdrew to the mountain side to pray a while. He would rejoin them later.

The disciples entered the ship and put out from the shore. But after some minutes the waters became rough and the boat was tossed on the waves, threatening to overturn.

Jesus, from the high place where he was praying, saw his disciples in danger and went to them, walking on the water.

It was night; and the disciples, dimly seeing this figure walking on the lake, were frightened and started to cry out:

'It is a ghost!'

Then Jesus reassured them:

'Do not be afraid. It is I.'

But Peter, unconvinced, said:

'Master, if it be really thou, command me to come to thee over the water.'

'Come,' replied Jesus simply.

Peter let himself down out of the boat and started walking on the water too, but then, seeing that the wind was becoming stronger, he felt that the waves would overwhelm him and he started to call out:

'Lord, save me!'

Jesus stretched out his hand, saying:

'Why dost thou doubt, man of little faith?' And he drew him with him to the boat.

Then the wind ceased and the lake became calm and still.

The disciples knelt down before Jesus and said to him:

'Truly thou art the Son of God.'

The Samaritan woman

SAINT JOHN tells of the episode of the Samaritan woman.

One day Jesus was passing through Samaria when, feeling tired, he sat down near a well.

While he was resting, a woman came with a jar to draw water. Jesus asked her for a drink, but she roughly replied:

'How is it that thou a Jew, dost ask a favour of me, a Samaritan?'

And Jesus replied:

'He who asks thee now for a drink is able to give one to thee instead, not well-water but living water, from the spring.'

Jesus meant that the living water was divine grace. But the woman, who was a sinner, did not understand until he showed that he knew her whole life story. Then she guessed that he must be the Christ.

82

The pearl

SAINT MATTHEW tells us the parable of the pearl.

A trader went in search of pearls. He found many ordinary ones, buying them and storing them for the future. Then one day he saw a very rare and beautiful pearl, more precious than all the others put together. So he sold all the less valuable ones to buy the precious pearl.

The pleasures of this world are trivial and unimportant and all together they are certainly not equal to the infinitely precious treasure of eternal life. It is worth renouncing all earthly goods to gain the joy of Paradise.

The lost sheep

IT is Saint Luke who tells us the parable of the lost sheep.

The Pharisees criticized Jesus because he was often in the company of sinners. So he told this parable.

If a shepherd has a hundred sheep and loses one, he will leave the ninety-nine who are safe and go looking for the lost one. And as soon as he has found it, he puts it on his shoulder, and takes it to the fold, saying joyfully to his friends: I have found the sheep which was lost. It is back with me once again.

By this parable Jesus wished to say: I am like a shepherd. I love my sheep very much and I wish to have them near me always. If then one abandons me to follow a path which leads him astray, I leave the others for the moment, and hurry in search of that one: when I have brought him back I am happy because I always rejoice when a sinner who has strayed from the true way returns to my kingdom.

So we see that Jesus is happy when a repentant sinner returns to the fold. But the sinner himself will feel the greatest happiness when he sees himself received with so much kindness, when he feels himself safe again under the protection of the good Shepherd who has generously forgiven him, and who is ready once more to give him the marvellous gifts of his divine heart.

For only by being close to Jesus, only by following his precious teachings, only by immense faith in his justice, can one find the strength to overcome every obstacle, and to accept suffering serenely.

The transfiguration

THIS beautiful scene is described by Saint Matthew, Saint Mark, and Saint Luke in their gospels.

This is Saint Matthew's story:

One day Jesus took Peter, James, and John with him and went up on a mountain side to pray. And while they were up there a marvellous thing took place. Suddenly the face of Jesus shone like the sun, his garments became white as snow. The figures of Moses, the Jewish lawgiver, and Elias the prophet also appeared with him—and they spoke together.

The three apostles were amazed and frightened. Peter stammered out some words, hardly knowing what he said. Then they were enveloped in a bright cloud, and a voice out of the cloud said:

'This is my beloved Son: hearken to him.'

This made them fall on their faces in great fear. And the next thing they knew, Jesus had his hand on their shoulders and he was saying: 'Get up now. Do not be afraid.' They looked up and there he was, just himself alone.

Then the three apostles descended the mountain with him, filled with a great desire to tell everyone about what they had seen.

But while they were on the road Jesus exhorted them not to say anything for the moment. They would be able to speak later on, 'after the son of Man has risen from the dead'. That seemed the most puzzling thing that Jesus had ever said. 'What could it mean?' they asked one another.

The healing of the lunatic boy

THE following day Jesus, once more with his disciples, found a great crowd awaiting him. One man went up to him as soon as he saw him, holding his son by the hand, and saying:

'Lord, I entreat thee to heal my son who is possessed by the devil. Thy disciples were unable to cure him.' At that very moment the boy threw himself on the ground, seized by one of his usual attacks.

Then Jesus went up to the boy with convulsions and ordered the devil to leave him for ever. The boy immediately became calm, and Jesus took him by the hand and raised him up.

Later on, when the multitude had dispersed, proclaiming the miracle, the disciples asked Jesus: 'Why could we not cure that boy?'

Jesus answered: 'To drive away the devil one must fast and pray and have a very great faith, a faith that will move mountains.'

88

The healing of the deaf and dumb man

SAINT MARK and Saint Matthew both tell the miracle of the healing of the deaf and dumb man.

According to Saint Mark:

Jesus was travelling towards the Sea of Galilee, and the multitude as usual hurried to meet him to beg favours and to witness his miracles.

A deaf and dumb man was brought to him. Jesus took him aside, and touched his ears and mouth, saying:

'Be opened'—and immediately the man heard and began to speak.

His first words were of thanks to the Lord. And all those present were filled with awe.

'Jesus does everything perfectly,' they said. 'He can even give hearing to the deaf, and speech to the dumb.'

How great must the happiness of the deaf and dumb man have been when he found himself suddenly freed from the isolated world in which he had been confined! With what joy must he have listened to the words of his family! How gladly must he have given expression to all the affection he felt for his nearest and dearest, which he had never been able to put into words! Jesus performed other miracles that day. He tenderly received all the sufferers who were brought to him, giving sight to the blind, causing the lame to walk normally, healing the maimed and bringing happiness to those who were troubled. And he bade the witnesses of these miracles to keep silent about them. But it was impossible to keep such things secret. In fact the news had spread all over Galilee in a very short time, and everyone sought to see Jesus, to touch his robe, and to hear his words.

The good Samaritan

ONE day, a lawyer, unbelieving, wished to put Jesus to the test, and asked him:

'Master, what must I do in order to obtain eternal life?'

Jesus answered:

'Love the Lord thy God, with all thy heart, with all thy soul, with all thy strength, and with all thy mind; and thy neighbour as thyself.' Then, the better to help him understand, he told this parable:

As he was going to Jericho, a certain Jew came across some robbers who stripped him of all he had, wounding him, and leaving him abandoned on the road. Soon afterwards, there passed by two travellers both in the service of the Temple of Jerusalem, at a short distance from each other. Of course it was to be expected that they would stop immediately, and succour the unfortunate man; but neither did; each continued on his way, without deigning even to glance at him.

Then there passed by the place a Samaritan, one of those men who despised the Jews and were despised by them, but seeing the wounded man, he dismounted, attended to his wounds, and then putting him in the saddle, brought him to an inn. The morning after, before leaving, the good Samaritan paid the bill for the wounded man also, exhorting the inn-keeper to take good care of him and promising that if the money was insufficient, he would give him some more on his return.

After telling this parable, Jesus asked the lawyer:

'Which of these three men treated the wounded man as his neighbour?'

'The one who helped him,' replied the lawyer.

'And thou shalt treat thy neighbour as did the good Samaritan,' added Jesus.

To deserve Paradise we must love God: and God loves us if we do good to our neighbours, including not only our friends but also our enemies.

The prodigal son

THERE was once a very rich landowner who had two sons who helped him with the work in the fields, and of whom he was extremely fond.

But one day, the younger of these boys became bored by the quiet life which he led at his father's home. He went to his father and said:

'Father give me my share of the property.'

The father was saddened by this request, but not wishing to go against his son, he gave him that which was his due.

After some days the son took his inheritance and departed from his family.

He went away without regret from the house where he was born, where he had spent his childhood and had once worked happily with his father and brother.

He travelled far and wide and soon spent all his wealth. Reduced to poverty, he was obliged to ask others for help, but he obtained none, particularly since there was that year a great famine, and each man kept for himself what little he had. Thus the young man was reduced to starvation.

So he left the city and went in search of work.

He walked and walked, arriving one day at the house of a rich but very mean man, and he asked him for work. This man thought for a while and came to the conclusion that it would be a good bargain to take this poor

man, reduced by hunger, into his service, since he could take advantage of his need, making him work hard, and paying him very little.

The boy spent many sad days at the house of the unkind master, who treated servants and beasts alike.

He worked there as a swineherd, and, as the food which he received was not enough, he had to satisfy his hunger by taking the husks from the swine before they devoured them.

Often he sat, dirty, pale, and half-starved, among the animals, thinking

of the rich home which he had left, of his good and affectionate father, of his brother still working in peace and security! And often he repented of his folly. If only he could return to his father's home!

Eventually, one day, he made a decision. He said to himself: it is impossible to go on like this. I will return to my father and beg him to take me among his servants. At least I shall have enough bread to eat, like all the other servants of my family. So he left the swine and set off homewards.

The father, who had suffered greatly because of his son's departure, thought continually of the absent boy. One day, as he was standing in the doorway of the house, he saw a weary beggar approaching. He looked attentively at him, then trembling with emotion, cried:

'But it is my son!'

Without thinking of anything else, he ran to meet him and embraced him fondly and with great joy.

Then the boy said humbly to him:

'Father, I have sinned, and I am no longer worthy to be called thy son.'

But his father would not let him continue. He called together the members of the family, he caused the most beautiful garments to be brought, and dressed his son very magnificently, putting a valuable ring on his finger: then he commanded the fatted calf to be killed and gave orders that a rich banquet be prepared.

The feast had already begun when the brother returned from the fields.

Amazed by what he heard, he asked a servant:

'What has happened?'

The servant said that the master's other son had returned and had been received with great pomp: he told him about the orders which had been given.

Then this young man was greatly upset and refused even to enter the house, saying to his father when he came to ask him to join in the festivities:

'Thou art unjust. Thou hast never given me as much as a kid for a feast with my friends, and I have served thee faithfully for years remaining always at thy side; but thou hast killed the fatted calf for my brother, who has squandered his fortune.'

The father answered:

'Do not be offended but try to understand me. All that I now possess is thine. But how can I ignore the return of my other son, whom I believed to be lost for ever? I wish to welcome him warmly and I must rejoice.'

Through this parable Jesus wished us to realize that the heavenly Father is always ready to welcome a repentant sinner with joy.

Mary Magdalen

ONE day Jesus was invited to dinner by a certain man Simon. He had just sat down at table when a beautiful woman entered carrying an alabaster jar full of precious ointment. This woman was called Mary and lived at Magdala, and was therefore named Mary Magdalen. She was a sinner. Simon looked at her contemptuously, surprised that she should dare to enter.

But she approached Jesus, and knelt at his feet, bathing them with her tears. Then she dried them with her hair, and anointed them with the perfumed ointment.

Jesus patiently allowed her to do this, but Simon was wondering how Jesus could permit a sinner to act in this way. Then Jesus, who had read his thoughts said:

'Once a man had two debtors: one owed him much and the other only a little. But as they could not pay, the creditor forgave both their debts. Which of the two should have felt more grateful?'

'He who had the greater debt,' replied Simon.

98

'That is so,' said Jesus. 'And this woman also has shown her loving gratitude towards me because she knows that her many sins will be forgiven.'

Then turning to Mary Magdalen, he blessed her and sent her away, saying:

'Go in peace. Thy faith has saved thee.'

Martha and Mary

ONE day Jesus was on a journey and entered the house where Mary lived with her sister Martha.

As soon as they saw him the two women joyfully hurried to receive him with all honours.

And Martha immediately started preparing a meal. She was anxious that everything should be perfect as was fitting. She ran here and there, cooking the very best food, and preparing the table. Mary, instead, was seated at Jesus's feet, listening silently to his words. She did not bother about anything else. So Martha complained:

'Lord, look at my sister. She is seated comfortably at thy feet while I am so busy. Dost thou not think that she should help me instead?'

Jesus replied:

'Martha, Martha, thou art careful, and art troubled about many things.

'There is no need to worry unduly about earthly food, but that of the soul is the most important for it remains with us for ever.'

The widow's mite

SAINT MARK tells us of a widow's offering.

Jesus was in the first courtyard of the temple; it was here that the chests were in which the Jews placed their offerings.

Rich people passed by, and gave generously of their wealth.

Then a poor widow passed by; she had only two brass mites in her bag, but she took them and dropped them down one of the great horns on top of the chest.

Jesus looked at her with tenderness and said to his disciples:

'Did you see? This poor widow has given more than all the rich men, because those who have much have given only the surplus, while she has given all that she possessed. She is worthy of great honour.'

103

The raising of Lazarus

SAINT JOHN continues the story.

One day Jesus, with his disciples, was beyond the river Jordan, when a message reached him from Martha and Mary saying that their brother Lazarus was very ill. The two sisters begged Jesus to come to their home. He was not able to go immediately and when he arrived Lazarus had already died and was buried.

Martha came weeping to meet him, and said:

'If thou hadst been here, my brother would not now be dead.'

'Thy brother will rise again,' Jesus replied to her. And he continued: 'I am the resurrection and the life. He who believes in me, though he is dead, will live on. And he who lives and believes in me will never die. . . . Dost thou believe it, Martha?'

'I believe it,' answered the woman: 'I know that thou art the Son of God.'

In the meantime Mary also had been told of his arrival, and ran to meet Jesus, repeating, between her tears, the same words as her sister. Jesus was very moved, and asked:

'Where is the dead man?'

'Come and see,' said the sisters. And they brought him to the tomb, which consisted of a cave, sealed by a big stone.

'Take away the stone,' said Jesus.

Then Martha said: 'But our brother has already been dead four days.'

Jesus replied: 'Have I not told thee that if thou believest thou wilt see that God's power is limitless.'

As the stone was being taken away, Jesus raised his eyes to heaven and said:

'Father, I thank thee for having heard me.' He remained a little longer in prayer, and then ordered in a loud, clear voice:

'Lazarus, come forth.'

Then, to everyone's amazement, Lazarus came out from the tomb, just as he had been put there, still wrapped in burial clothes.

Jesus added:

'Loose him, and let him go free.'

This was done and Lazarus returned home with his sisters.

Jesus drives the merchants out of the temple

On two occasions Jesus was greatly saddened by something that happened.

Entering the Temple he found that it was occupied by merchants who were selling and bargaining for cattle and livestock.

Full of indignation, Jesus took a whip, and with many reproaches drove

the merchants and their animals out of the Temple, saying: 'My house is a house of prayer but you have made it a den of thieves.'

The Jews asked him how he dared to do such a thing.

Jesus replied that should they destroy the Temple, he could rebuild it in three days.

Jesus, however, did not mean the real Temple; he meant his own body which he would bring to life again after three days.

The Pharisees against Jesus

THE resurrection of Lazarus made a great impression on the Pharisees, and the chief priests, who were already worried by the enthusiasm which Jesus called forth everywhere, so they thought it necessary to take immediate steps when faced by this new miracle.

They, therefore, summoned a meeting of the Council in the Temple forecourt and said:

'This man is becoming a danger to us. If we allow him to continue, everyone will believe in him and we shall be discredited.'

One of them, Caiaphas, who was High Priest that year, added: 'This man is a danger to the nation; it would be better if he were to die. It is fitting that one man should die to save the people.' He did not realize the full truth of his words.

'But not on a feast day,' they replied, lest there be a disturbance among the people.

From then on, their one idea was to find a way of carrying out their plot, a way that would be safe for themselves.

The triumphal entry into Jerusalem

ALL four evangelists tell this tale in their gospels. According to Saint Mark:

One day while his enemies were planning how they could have him killed, Jesus started off for Jerusalem. On arriving near Mount Olivet, he said to his disciples:

'Go to the village over the way and at the entrance you will find an ass's foal tied to a tree. Untie it, and bring it here. If anyone asks you why, say: "The Lord has need of it."'

The disciples obeyed. Then, placing their cloaks on the foal's back, they helped Jesus to mount, and they set out together for Jerusalem. Word having reached them that Jesus was coming, the inhabitants turned out in great numbers to meet him, waving palms in greeting, and laying their cloaks and garments on the ground in his path, all crying out:

'Hosanna: blessed is he that cometh in the name of the Lord: Hosanna in the highest of heavens.'

A wave of enthusiasm soon spread all over the city. The few who did not know him went to the doors asking:

'Who is he?'

'It is the prophet Jesus,' replied the people.

Accompanied by these acclamations Jesus entered into the Temple.

The Last Supper

A WAY of bringing about the destruction of Jesus was suggested to the chief priests by one of Jesus's own followers, one of the very twelve whom he had chosen, Judas Iscariot. This man went to the chief priests, and promised to hand over Jesus to them for a reward of thirty pieces of silver. But Jesus, who knew all, knew also of this betrayal.

Meanwhile the feast of the Passover was at hand and the disciples asked Jesus:

'Where dost thou wish us to prepare the meal this evening?' Jesus answered:

'Go into the city; there you will meet a man with a jar of water. Follow him and where he enters, enter you also, and ask the owner of the house

112

the way to the room where the Master will eat with his disciples. He will show it to you.'

The disciples obeyed. Two of them entered the city, and there they saw the man with the jar of water as Jesus had said; they followed him and came to a house where the owner, who was expecting them, showed them to a large room and said: 'Make your preparations here.'

Towards evening, Jesus arrived with his other apostles and they all sat down at table.

At a certain moment, while they were still eating, Jesus said with great sadness: 'One of you will betray me.'

The apostles looked at one another astonished and asked him: 'Who will betray thee?'

And Jesus answered: 'One of the twelve who puts his hand into the dish with me. But woe to him! It would be better for him had he never been born.'

The disciples still did not understand. Then John, whom he loved so much, begged him:

'Dost thou mean to tell me that I will betray thee?'

Jesus replied:

'It is he to whom I offer a piece of bread.' He dipped the bread in the dish and gave it to Judas Iscariot.

Then the traitor immediately arose and went out. It was deep night.

It was on this night before he suffered that Jesus took bread, then, after a brief prayer, broke it and gave it to his apostles saying: 'Take, eat; this is my body.' And he took the cup, and when he had given thanks he gave it to them saying: 'Drink this, all of you: this is my blood; the blood which I shall shed for you and for all mankind. Do this in memory of me.'

The great promise, recounted by Saint John, that Jesus had made after feeding the five thousand was fulfilled. This time he did not multiply bread or change water into wine, but changed bread into his own Body and changed wine into his own Blood, yet so that they looked the same and tasted the same as before.

And so with these words Jesus established the Holy Eucharist and gave the greatest proof of his love. He not only gave Himself as food to the apostles on that night but, when he said: 'Do this in memory of me,' he made them priests for ever with power to offer this very same sacrifice to the Eternal Father. By it the memorial of his passion would be renewed, his very life would come into the souls of men, and they would look forward to sitting with him at table, so to say, in the Kingdom of his Father. This explains why he longed to eat *this* Pasch with them which gives perfect meaning to his own saying, 'I am the life.'

It is Saint John who also tells us that when supper was done Jesus washed the feet of his disciples. It was his last act of loving humility.

Thursday evening

SAINT MATTHEW tells us:

When he left the supper room, Jesus went with his disciples to Mount Olivet.

He was very sad. He said to them.

'This night sad events will take place and you will abandon me.'

'I will never leave thee,' answered Peter. 'I tell thee, Peter,' answered Jesus, 'thou wilt deny me thrice before the cock crows.'

'I will not deny thee,' said Peter again.

'We will never deny thee,' repeated the disciples together.

Jesus took his eleven disciples with him and went towards the place called Gethsemane. Having made the rest sit down, he took apostles Peter, James, and John, apart and said to them:

'My soul is ready to die with sorrow. Remain here, and watch with me.'

Then he went a little farther away, and he fell on his face on the earth and prayed:

'Father, if thou be willing, remove this cup from me.'

He remained there a little longer in prayer, then he went up to the apostles and, with sorrow, saw that they were sleeping.

Then he said:

'Was it not even possible for you to watch one hour with me?' And he exhorted them: 'Watch and pray.' Then he turned back and knelt down, saying:

'My Father, if this cup cannot pass away unless I drink it, thy will be done.'

He felt a death-like cold; drops of sweat and blood broke out on his body. Then an angel came and comforted him.

He rose up, and approaching the apostles, who were still sleeping, said:

'Let us go; my hour has arrived. The traitor is close at hand.'

He had scarcely finished speaking, when he saw Judas, surrounded by a band of armed soldiers, to whom the traitor had already said: 'He whom I shall kiss is Jesus. Take him.'

*　　　　*　　　　*　　　　*

How much heartfelt grief in the words: My soul is ready to die with sorrow. Remain here, and watch with me.

What did the disciples reply to him?

We do not know. We only know that it was not very effective, because Jesus's grief did not pass. They certainly promised not to abandon him. But with no great enthusiasm. They were tired and they probably said

116

the first words which came to their lips, without stopping to think of the actual significance.

In fact they were not true to their word because they fell asleep.

They did worse: they denied the Master and Jesus knew all this.

And he also knew that he must suffer derision, blows and insults in exchange for all the good which he had brought to the world.

He knew it and he accepted it without murmur because he, the Son of God, had come on earth only for the purpose of saving suffering humanity.

But although he knew it, he was unable to banish the terrible grief which afflicted his soul, just as his body was later to be afflicted by the scourging, the blows, and the crown of thorns placed on his head by his tormentors.

Jesus had to suffer everything to save us.

But the grief which burdened his pure spirit was intense, and he, bowed down on his knees, with his face bent to the ground, gave that imploring cry:

'Father, if thou be willing, remove this cup from me.'

He was exhausted, overcome, and all the while his beloved disciples only slept.

And seeing it, this also added to his suffering.

A last time, he begged them to watch, knowing, however, that they would fall asleep once more and he threw himself on the earth, and his tortured soul cried out again to his Father in his sorrow.

But he no longer prayed him to let the bitter chalice pass him by. Instead he said:

'. . . however not as I wish, but as thou wishest.'

He is the spotless Lamb ready for the supreme sacrifice for those who love him, for those who hate him, for those who are not yet born.

But the sorrow is grievous and the effort to overcome it, supreme.

Then Jesus rises, calmed. He returns to the apostles and sees them still sleeping. But this time he makes no reproach.

He puts himself entirely in his Father's hands and nothing can touch him any more. If only human beings would surrender themselves with complete faith to the heavenly Father, how much easier life would be, and how much less man would suffer!

To give ourselves into God's hands, to accept with resignation and unwavering faith all that he sends us, believing that he is truly our Father and, as such, desires only our happiness: such is wisdom indeed.

Guided by Judas the executioners arrived. They were many; a throng: porters, door-keepers, ignorant people who were taking part in this shameful deed only for the money promised them by the leaders. They were all armed; armed to meet twelve men, with only two swords among them. And Judas pressed his lips to the pure face of Jesus.

That kiss of betrayal was more repellent than any insult or blow.

The Son of God spoke to the traitor. Then, with no sign of anger, he asked the crowd:

'Whom are you seeking?'
'Jesus of Nazareth,' came the reply.
'I am he,' he said, with such infinite dignity that some fell to the ground

in fear. He repeated his question, showing that he was Master and then, out of concern for his disciples, added: 'I have told you who I am. Therefore let those who are here go away.'

Then the soldiers arrested him. But Simon Peter could not restrain his wrath: and drawing his sword, he flung himself on one of Caiaphas' servants and cut off his ear. But Jesus who wanted no violence said to Peter:

'Why hast thou done this? Violence can only incite violence.
Dost thou not know that if I wished I could summon twelve
legions of angels to defend me?

'Believe me: it must be as it is.'

Then he was led away between the soldiers. And the disciples
deserted him.

122

Jesus before the priests

PETER, however, followed Jesus as far as the High Priest's house, where the chief priests and the others who sought his death were assembled. He entered after Jesus and sat down in the forecourt with the servants.

125

The chief priests roughly questioned those present in order to discover evidence against Jesus. But they could find none because he had never done any ill.

Finally some people said:

'This man has alleged that he could destroy the Temple of God and rebuild it in three days.'

Then the High Priest stood up and asked Jesus:

'It *is* true that thou hast said this?' But Jesus did not reply.

Caiaphas again asked him:

'Answer: is it true that thou art the Christ, the Son of God?'

'It *is* true,' the Nazarene then replied, 'and before very long you will see me seated at his right hand, and coming on the clouds of heaven.'

At these words the High Priest, who was very angry, cried out:

'He blasphemes. Surely we have need of no further witnesses?'

'No, no, enough!' shouted those present. 'Let him be put to death!' Then they mocked and blindfolded him, spat in his face and injured him with their blows, calling out: 'Prophesy, O Christ, who struck thee?'

Peter's denial

IN the forecourt Peter met a maid-servant who remarked:

'Thou too wast with Jesus of Nazareth.'

'Thou art mistaken,' denied Peter in front of all.

Just as he left the place, he met another maid-servant, who after looking well at him, cried out:

'This man also was with Jesus the Nazarene.'

Peter said again:

'I do not know that man.'

But several people went up to him saying:

'Thou art truly one of his disciples.'

Then Peter replied vehemently:

'It is not true. I know him not.'

He had denied the divine Master three times.

At that moment the cock crowed. Then
Peter remembered the words of Jesus, and
he wept bitterly.

Meanwhile Judas, realizing the wrong he
had done to Jesus, was filled with remorse,
and went to the priests taking back the
money and saying: 'My master is innocent.
I was wrong.' But the priests, who had no
further use for him, replied: 'That is thy
concern.'

Then Judas threw the money down before
the priests and went away and hanged
himself.

Jesus before Pilate and Herod

IN the morning Jesus was brought to the house of the Roman governor, Pontius Pilate, so that the sentence, given by the Jewish judges, might be confirmed by him. Pontius Pilate gazed in astonishment at this man whom they brought before him as a criminal, and who bore no resemblance to such; then he asked the Jewish judges:

'What has he done?'

128

They replied.

'He goes about preaching doctrines contrary to our religion and against the Roman government; and he alleges that he is Christ, King of the Jews.'

'Is it true that thou art the King of the Jews?' Pilate asked Jesus.

'My kingdom,' said Jesus, 'is not of this world.'

But the chief priests would not let him speak again; railing against him incessantly, and accusing him of crimes which he had not committed.

'Dost thou not hear how they accuse thee?' said Pilate again. 'Defend thyself.' But Jesus did not reply.

Pilate then said to the accusers:

'I do not find this man should be condemned to death.'

But, implacable, the accusers only repeated:

'Thou deceivest thyself. He has been inciting the people to revolt. He started in Galilee and has continued as far as here and he is sure to continue.'

'In Galilee?' Pilate was only too pleased to hear this because Galilee was not under his jurisdiction, but that of Herod, a cruel and wicked ruler who was at that very moment in Jerusalem for the Paschal feast. Pleased to be rid of him, Pilate sent Jesus to Herod so that he should decide on his fate.

Herod had already heard a great deal about this amazing man and, though he had wanted to, he had never seen him. He immediately told him to perform some miracle. But Jesus completely ignored his request and though Herod asked him many questions, Jesus made no reply. Irritated by this behaviour, and urged on by the chief priests who were ceaseless in their accusations, Herod treated Jesus as a madman and, assisted by his soldiers, he began to mock him. He had him dressed in a white tunic, a sign of madness, then, surrounded by his enemies, who derided him and laughed in his face, he was taken through the streets of Jerusalem back to Pilate.

Then Pilate assembled the chief priests and the leaders of the people and repeated:

'Neither Herod nor I find that this man deserves to be sent to his death. We will give him a punishment and let him go free.'

But the accusers were not of the same idea.

Then Pilate remembered the custom which there was at Jerusalem of liberating a prisoner at the time of the Paschal feast.

There was a dangerous prisoner in the prison, a man called Barabbas, who, among other things, had also committed a murder. So Pilate said: 'Do you wish me to free Jesus or Barabbas?'

He was hoping that they would reply: 'Jesus.'

But, instead, the leaders of the people cried out:

'Let Barabbas go free and crucify Jesus!'

Pilate repeated with insistence:

'Jesus does not really deserve crucifixion! If you wish I will give him a punishment; I will have him scourged.'

But the accusers, infuriated, started to shout, swear, and threaten until Pilate promised to let Barabbas go free.

130

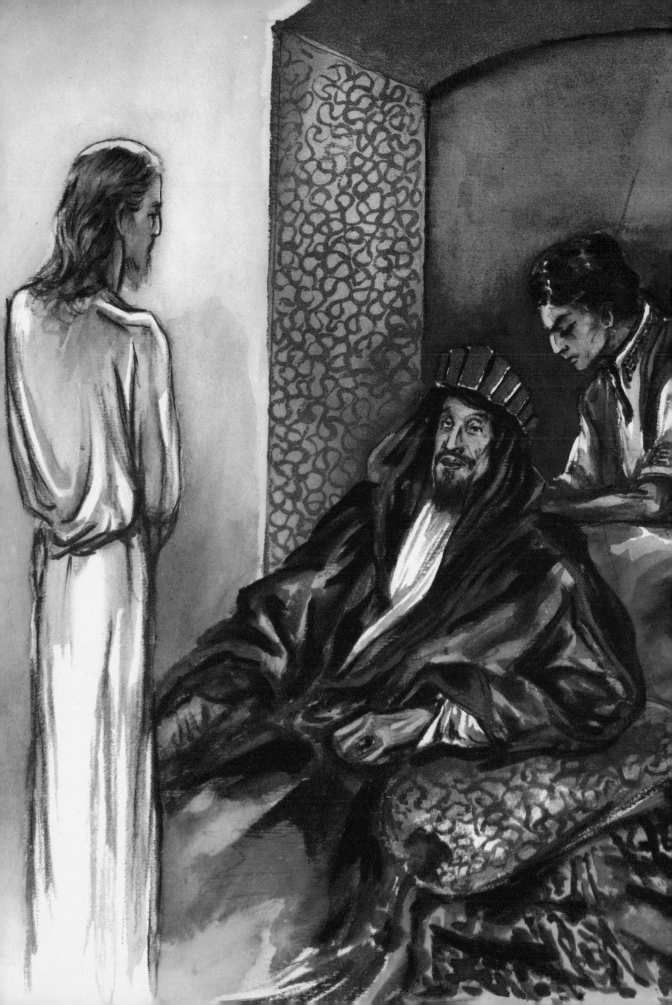

'*ECCE HOMO*'

NOW Saint John tells us the rest of this tragic story:

And so the final martyrdom of Jesus began. The soldiers took off his garments, they bound him to a post and scourged him with a whip made of leather strips. Then, not content with tormenting his body, they endeavoured also to wound his soul by holding him up to ridicule. They put a scarlet cloak on his shoulders, a crown of thorns on his head, and thrusting a reed into his hand, cried out, 'Behold the King of the Jews!' Then they started beating him, spitting in his face, and pushing the crown down on to his head until the thorns drove deep into him, causing rivulets of blood to spurt forth.

Pilate, hoping that the people would be moved by this spectacle, took Jesus by the arm, and leading him on to the outer terrace, said:

'Behold this man. Do you not see to what a state he is reduced?'

But the ferocious crowd roared savagely:

'Crucify him! Crucify him!'

'But why crucify him when he has done no wrong?' Pilate asked, not wishing to stain himself with the blood of this innocent man.

'He has committed outrages against our religion; he ought to die because he claims to be the Son of God.'

Pilate was all the more afraid and again begged Jesus to deny his guilt; and as Jesus remained silent he said to him:

'But speak! Dost thou not know that I have power to save or crucify thee?'

Then Jesus replied:

'Thou wouldst not have any power over me at all if it were not given thee from heaven.'

Meanwhile the people continued to cry out:

'If thou release this man thou art not a friend of Caesar.'

These words worried Pilate greatly as he was afraid of being denounced to Rome as a traitor.

However, before approving such an unjust sentence, he wished to make one last attempt.

He once more showed Jesus, scourged and crowned with thorns, hoping
that they would be moved. And he said: 'Behold your King.'
But the crowd started shouting again:
'We have no other king but Caesar.'
Then he realized that there was nothing else he could do.
However Pilate did not wish to bear the responsibility of this unjust

condemnation. He had a bowl full of water brought, and, in the presence of all, he washed his hands, saying:

'I am not guilty of the blood of this innocent man. It is your affair.'

And the people cried out:
'His blood be upon us and upon our children.'
Then Pilate set Barabbas free and handed Jesus over to the enraged mob.

Journey to the Cross

SAINT LUKE, Saint Matthew, Saint John, and Saint Mark all speak of the tragic death of Jesus. Let us hear a little from each of the four.

Saint Luke begins:

Jesus's cloak was removed and he was given back his seamless robe which had been woven all in one piece. The crown of thorns was left on his head and a cross of wood placed on his shoulders, then, with the two thieves who were to be executed with him, they made him walk towards Golgotha.

The cross was very heavy and Jesus, who had already been tortured, was at the end of his strength; after a short distance, the soldiers realized that he could not possibly go on. Then they called a man from Cyrene, who was returning from the country, and they made him carry the cross. The sad procession continued. There were great numbers of people. During the walk many women joined in, and some supported Mary, the mother of Jesus who gazed in desolation at her son whom she was helpless to assist.

140

It was almost midday when they arrived at the place of execution, called Calvary. The soldiers undressed Jesus, laying him with outspread arms on the cross, which was extended on the ground, and there they drove the nails through his hands and feet. And Jesus said: 'Father, forgive them, for they do not know what they are doing.'

Saint John adds:

High up, on the cross, they nailed a notice with these words, written by Pilate: 'Jesus of Nazareth. King of the Jews'.

But the chief priests, angry and bitter to the end, said to Pilate that he should have written instead 'This man said: I am King of the Jews'.

But Pilate, still annoyed by the injustice of the condemnation, replied: 'Thus have I written, and thus shall it remain.'

Then the cross, with its divine burden, was raised up between those of the two thieves. The soldiers divided the garments of Jesus between them, and cast lots for his seamless robe.

The people who loved the Nazarene stood by gazing at the sad sight, unhappy because they were unable to help their Master.

141

Saint John tells us, expressly, that our Lord's Mother stood by the cross as he, the beloved disciple, did also. When Jesus saw them both standing there he said to his Mother: 'Behold thy son' and to Saint John: 'Behold thy Mother.' She was the last gift he gave mankind before he died.

But those Jews who had always hated him, mocked him even to the last, crying out insolently:

'If it is true that thou art the King of the Jews, save thyself.'

'And why dost thou not save us also?' added one of the thieves angrily.

The other instead uttered words of love and repentance. Then Jesus said to him: 'This day thou shalt be with me in Paradise.'

Saint Mark gives us this information:

After three hours of agony, Jesus cried out with a voice filled with suffering:

'My God, My God, why hast thou abandoned me?' Then: 'I thirst.'

One of the soldiers offered him a sponge dipped in vinegar, fixed on a lance.

Jesus just wetted his lips, and called out to the heavenly Father in a loud and triumphant voice 'It is finished,' lowered his head and died.

Saint Matthew tells us of all the horror which followed the death of Jesus.

A great wind came up, flash after flash of lightning cut across the black heavens, the earth trembled, rocks split apart, and tombs opened up and many dead arose from the grave.

Terrified, the soldiers fled, and their centurion said: 'Truly he was the Son of God!'

*   *   *   *

Christ is dead. This man who gave sight to the blind, speech to the dumb, who raised up the dead, who placed his hands so lovingly on the heads of little children, and who brought salvation to lost souls, has breathed his last breath in a supreme invocation to the heavenly Father:

'Father, I commit my soul into thy hands.'

His head drooping to one side, his eyes clouded, his lips livid, cracked by the burning of the fever, this is the state to which he has been reduced, this man who loved men so much and who came to earth to save them.

The executioners have fled, in terror. But the holy women, Mary (his mother), Mary Magdalen, and Mary of Cleophas have not gone away and, kneeling beside the cross, are filled with horror and desolation as they look at the divine Martyr who lives no more.

So the deed is fulfilled.

And the cross lives and will live for all eternity to gather into its protective shade all who weep and seek comfort.

The crucified bodies had to be taken away. The Jews did not want such a sight to cloud the Paschal festivities: they wanted to enjoy themselves, to be merry, threatened by no fear of remorse. They sent a message to Pilate that he should have the condemned men buried.

The order was given and immediately carried out. Some soldiers came up to the crosses, and broke the legs of the two thieves with an iron bludgeon to shorten their agony in case they were not already dead.

But there was no need of this for Jesus. All had seen him die. However, a soldier called Longinus pierced Jesus's side with his spear, just to make sure. And, immediately, there flowed forth blood and water, to the amazement of all.

Now nothing was heard on the desolate height save the weeping of the women, who could find no peace.

Christ is taken down from the Cross

SAINT MATTHEW continues:

When evening came, a rich man of Arimathea, called Joseph, went to Pilate and asked him to give him Jesus's body. Having obtained this favour, he took a white sheet, and going to Calvary, with utmost care, removed the divine body from the cross, wrapping it in a sheet, and in the presence of the holy women, he put it in a tomb hollowed out of rock. Then he closed the tomb with a great stone and went away.

But the day after, the chief priests and Pharisees went to Pilate and said:

'We have remembered that this criminal affirmed that three days after his death he would rise again. Therefore, order that the tomb be guarded until the third day, because we do not want the body to be carried away by his followers who will then say that their Master has risen from the dead.'

Pilate replied:

'You have guards. Do as you wish.'

Then the Pharisees went to the sepulchre; they sealed the stone, and placed soldiers on guard before it who were to remain there all night.

But with the dawn came a tremendous noise, and the earth shook. The terrified soldiers saw at the mouth of the tomb, an angel in dazzling white robes who rolled back the stone and then sat himself thereon.

For a moment the guards were rooted to the spot in terror, but then they took to their heels, and fled.

The holy women before the sepulchre

SAINT MARK now tells us:

In the early hours of the morning Mary Magdalen, Salome, Mary mother of James and other holy women, went to the sepulchre carrying spices and perfumed ointments to embalm Jesus's body. On the way they said:

'How shall we open the sepulchre? The stone is heavy. It will be too difficult for us to move.'

They arrived with the first uneasy light of dawn, and were exceedingly surprised to find the tomb open. Mary Magdalen, without saying anything, turned back hurriedly to go and warn Simon Peter that the Master's body had been stolen. The others, instead, advanced cautiously, and when they looked into the cave they saw there a shining angel who said:

'Be not afraid. You are looking for Jesus the Nazarene. He is risen. You must look for him among the living, not the dead. Go and tell Peter and the other disciples that he will rejoin them in Galilee.'

Jesus appears to Mary Magdalen

WE now turn to Saint John:

Meanwhile Peter, who had been informed about the empty tomb by Mary Magdalen, hurried immediately to the place with another disciple. Seeing the sepulchre open, Peter entered, while his companion stopped at the entrance. They both saw the linen cloth in which Jesus had been wrapped lying on the stone ledge and, folded neatly apart, a small kerchief (which may have covered his head).

The Master had really disappeared yet there was nothing about the tomb which suggested robbery. John, at least, came away with the beginning of belief in the resurrection of his Master and Friend.

Meanwhile Mary Magdalen, who had returned, was weeping and praying beside the empty tomb when she suddenly saw within two angels dressed in white.

'Why dost thou weep?' they said.

And she answered:

'I am weeping because they have taken away my Lord, and I do not know where they have laid him.'

Hardly had she finished speaking when she heard a voice close behind her:

'Why dost thou weep?'

She turned round and saw a man smiling kindly at her. Thinking it was the owner of the garden, she repeated:

'They have stolen my Lord. If thou knowest where they have taken him, tell me.'

Then the man called to her in his gentle voice:

'Mary!'

She recognized him. Filled with unspeakable joy, she rose up crying out:

'Master!' and was about to throw herself at his feet. But Jesus raised her saying:

'Wait. Go now to my disciples and tell them that I must ascend to my Father and yours, to my God and your God.'

Mary Magdalen ran at once to announce the great event to the apostles. But they did not believe it could be true.

A mysterious traveller

LET us now hear what Saint Luke tells us:

That same day, two disciples were going to Emmaus, a village not very far from Jerusalem.

At a certain point a third traveller joined them, and asked:

'Why are you so sad?'

One of the two, called Cleophas, replied:

'I can tell that you do not come from these parts, otherwise you would know all about what has happened,' and they told him of the great prophet, Jesus of Nazareth, of the good which he had done, and of his tragic death.

'We really believed that he had come to save the people of Israel. Certain women claim that he has risen from the dead. However, no one has seen him.'

The mysterious traveller said:

'If Jesus was truly the Messiah he had to endure all that he suffered. Do you not remember the prophecies referring to him?' And he enumerated them all, drawing attention to the fact that they had all come true.

Meanwhile they had arrived at Emmaus and the third traveller was

about to take his leave. But Cleophas and his companion remarked that night was coming on, and invited him to stay with them. When it was supper time they all sat down at table, and the stranger took a loaf of bread, blessed it, broke it, offered it to his companions.

Only then did the two astonished disciples realize they were in the presence of Jesus. They were about to throw themselves at his feet with joyous cries, but he was already gone, as mysteriously as he had appeared.

Losing no time, the disciples immediately returned to Jerusalem to tell the apostles what had happened.

Jesus appears to the apostles

WHEN Cleophas and his companion arrived, tired and breathless, they found the apostles and other disciples, all together in a room, with the doors and windows closed for fear of the Jews.

'Open to us,' they cried, 'we have great news to tell.'

Some of the disciples opened the door and barred it again immediately after letting them enter. Then the two related what had happened to them after hearing that the Lord had indeed appeared to Simon Peter. Suddenly they raised their eyes and saw the divine Master before them. How had he entered? No one had let him in.

'Peace be with you,' said Jesus. And seeing their fright, he added: 'It is really I, do not be afraid.'

But the disciples were not convinced and they thought he was a ghost.

Then Jesus continued:

'Do you not believe me? Look at my hands and my feet which still bear the wounds of the nails.'

However, Jesus wanted to give another proof and he asked for food. They offered him a roast fish and a honeycomb. He ate, and then he gave his disciples what was left over. Thus they were all convinced that it was really Jesus in the flesh, and not a spirit. Only the body has need of material food.

'Are you convinced now?' asked Jesus looking into the eyes of the apostles. 'Was there really need of this material proof? And yet I always told you what would come to pass. Now go forth into the world and preach my gospel to all creatures.'

As the risen One spoke, the faces of the apostles became diffused with joyous light one after another.

It really was Jesus, the Son of God, the great Master. He had not abandoned them as they had feared. Now he had returned among his disciples to advise, guide, and protect them.

The disciples gazed at him, happy, exultant, but also afraid, because of the shameful way they had abandoned him, which now weighed on their consciences filling them with great remorse.

But Jesus, always good and generous, had no wish to add to their shame with words of reproof.

Instead he treated them as friends, and even gave them power to restore men to God's friendship, saying: 'Whose sins you shall forgive, they are forgiven.'

Thomas's lack of faith

NOW Saint John speaks to us of doubting Thomas.

The evening of Jesus's appearance, one of the twelve apostles was absent and had not seen Jesus. As soon as he returned, his companions hurried to meet him and told him of the great event. But Thomas shook his head, and said:

'Unless I see the marks of the nails and touch the wounds with my own hands, I cannot believe.'

The apostles were upset at these words and remained silent.

A week passed by and the disciples were again assembled in the same house, with the doors and windows closed as before, but this time Thomas was there too. Suddenly, while the disciples were talking, they saw Jesus before them.

'Peace be with you,' he said. Then he turned to Thomas:

'Thomas, why wilt thou not believe if thou dost not see? Nevertheless, touch my pierced hands, also put thy finger to my side, and be convinced.'

But Thomas did not dare to touch Jesus. It was enough for him to see to believe; and he threw himself at the divine Master's feet exclaiming:

'My Lord and my God!'

Then Jesus said:

'Thou hast believed because thou hast seen. Blessed are those who have not seen and who have believed.'

And Thomas who needed so much proof to convince him of the truth became a convincing witness for those who would never see. His faith was now unquestioning and his change of heart was apparent in his cry of love and joy:

'My Lord and my God!'

He no longer had any doubt. He knew with complete conviction that Jesus was his only Master, Lord of heaven and earth. Light had returned to his mind and his heart, never again to be extinguished.

With the other Apostles he was ready now to fulfil the command which Jesus gave a few days later in Galilee:

'Go and make disciples of all nations, baptizing them in the name of the Father, and of the Son, and of the Holy Ghost, teaching them to do all that I have taught you.'

*   *   *   *

There are still unfortunately those who do not believe because they do not see.

They are those who close their eyes when confronted with the light of faith, too radiant a light for their weak sight. They are those who live in the endless dark of a starless night and, attracted by material things alone,

162

believe only in what promises immediate gain: riches, well-being, honours, earthly pleasures.

But what are these advantages, which at the most last a human lifetime, in comparison with the heavenly blessings which endure for eternity? Among the unbelievers there are also unfortunately those who would drag down with them little children, whose eyes are already open towards heaven, and whose souls are full of light.

Saint Peter

ONE evening Peter, with some other apostles, went to fish on the lake of Tiberias. They fished all night without catching anything, and they were returning disappointedly towards the shore at dawn, when they saw Jesus there.

But they did not recognize him immediately.

He asked:

'Friends, have you nothing to eat?'

'No,' they replied.

Then Jesus suggested:

'Throw the net to the right of the boat.'

The fishermen obeyed; and at once the nets became so full that they could hardly pull them into the boat.

They found hot cinders by the lake side, ready for cooking the fish.

When the meal was ready, Jesus said:

'Come and eat,' and he himself distributed the bread and fish.

How great must have been the disciples' joy when Jesus appeared to them again like this!

When they had eaten, Jesus called Simon Peter and asked him, affectionately:

'Peter, dost thou love me above all?'

'Certainly,' replied Peter, kneeling down. 'Thou knowest that I love thee.'

'Then feed my lambs,' said Jesus to him.

'Peter, dost thou love me more than the others?'

'Thou knowest already that I love thee,' replied Peter.

'Then tend my yearlings,' said Jesus. Then, again:

'Dost thou love me?'

Peter again replied:

'Lord, thou knowest all: and thou knowest also that I love thee greatly.'

'Then tend my sheep,' said Jesus.

With these words he entrusted his sheep, that is his faithful, to Peter, and gave him the highest position in the whole Church.

Then, before leaving him, he predicted Peter's martyrdom.

The Ascension

Saint Luke tells us:

Forty days had passed since the Paschal feast, when Jesus, having assembled his apostles, led them to the Mount of Olives.

It was a wonderful day; the trees were all in blossom, the birds sang joyously from their nests, hidden among the tender green foliage. The air was warm and scented.

Up on the mountain, surrounded by the apostles, Jesus gazed into the distance, thinking of the life he had spent on earth. He remembered his sweet childhood at Nazareth, in the neat, pleasant little house; he thought of the first days of his public life, the crowd's enthusiasm, of the house at Bethany where Lazarus and his sisters always received him so joyously. Then he remembered the accusations of the Jews, their hate, of how they had condemned him to death . . . and then he felt a deep sadness. But he quickly smiled. He looked lovingly at the apostles and then he blessed them. And, while he was doing so, he rose from the ground and ascended towards heaven. He ascended into the air, framed against the clear blue sky by a dazzling light.

As he rose up he blessed men, all men, even those who had done him harm. Then, slowly, he disappeared: a cloud of purple and gold hid him from the sight of the apostles who worshipped him, and returned to Jerusalem rejoicing because this was his hour of triumph.

Then two angels, dressed in shining white, descended among them and said:

'Jesus has been taken up to heaven: he has gone into his kingdom.'

*   *   *   *

This is the truest and most beautiful story in the world.